Reaching for Rain

Young people finding hope in the storms of life

By Cindy Mosley

Reaching for Rain:
Young people finding hope in the storms of life

ISBN: 978-0-692-80223-6

Printed in USA by

DEDICATIONS

To God be the glory for the great thing He has done and is still doing in my life.

To Frank: Your patience and encouragement mean so much. It is great having a personal cheerleader following me around the house.

To my children & Jacobie: I love you all so much. I hope that the life I lived before you always point you to Christ. Thank you for the most beautiful grandchildren on the planet!

To my parents and parents-in-love: You have created a legacy of "touching lives with love" that I hope to always pursue. Thank you.

To Jessica, Darl, and Tony: You actually make being the middle child fun! I've learned so much from all of you.

To those of you who read these pages, you flatter and humble me with your enthusiasm to see what comes next. God bless you and keep you.

Always keep reaching for hope.

TABLE OF CONTENTS

Introduction

Chapter 1: Reach for Rain

Chapter 2: Jeremy's Rain

Chapter 3: Devan's Rain

Chapter 4: Logan's Rain

Chapter 5: Jonah's Rain

Chapter 6: Kenzie's Rain

Chapter 7: Sadie's Rain

Chapter 8: Chaz's rain

Chapter 9: After the Rain

Acknowledgements

About the Author

INTRODUCTION

Do you ever feel like an outsider, no matter where you are or what you do? You find yourself feeling lonely, even in a room full of people. At home, you don't even feel like you belong. You feel like you are an alien among normal people. You look around the classroom and wonder to yourself, *What is wrong with me? Why can't I be like? I wish somebody loved me.* Every day, the student next to you is dressed in the latest fashion, while you are lucky to get a new pair of shoes at the beginning of the school year. The student behind you is always talking about the fun stuff he does with his parents, such as going to games, fishing, or camping. You think to yourself, *I don't even know where my parents are. No, that's not true. I know where they are; they are somewhere, locked up, knocked up, or strung out, but not with me.* The kid in front of you is smart, makes straight A's, and is always smiling and helpful. Even your teachers seem to be happy all the time and you think there is no hope for you to ever find relief from your struggles so that you can just smile back at people, happy and at peace with life.

If you have ever experienced any of these feelings, you need to know that you are not alone. You may already have found a group of friends who are just as miserable as you are. I wish I could tell you that there is a magical formula to help you, but there isn't one. I do know of young people who have been where you are and have made it through. *Reaching for Rain* is a collection of stories about young people who found hope in unusual places and gained a fresh start. I hope you find warmth and inspiration within these stories and that you discover ways to share your victory over your dark days.

CHAPTER ONE

Reach for Rain

Rain refreshes
the Earth.
Rain recolors
landscapes.
Rain washes
away the dust.
Rain cools
the heat.
Rain replenishes
ponds.
Rain inspires
creativity.
Rain brings
hope.

Reach for Rain

By Ci Mosley

CHAPTER TWO
Jeremy's Rain

I sat on the porch at my grandparents' house while two police officers talked to them in the living room. They thought it best if I waited outside. I thought it was probably about one of my parents, because I hadn't seen either of them in almost a year. They were not together, but neither one of them was with me, either. I decided I wouldn't be surprised about what they were going to tell me. My parents were always in some sort of trouble. I had made up my mind a long time ago that I was not going to be like them. I would make something of myself and when I had children, I would be with them every day.

I heard footsteps coming toward the door. The police officers stepped out onto the porch. One of them stopped and sat beside me. "Jeremy, I'm Officer DeLoach, and I wanted to give you my card. I want you to know that you have someone on your side. If you ever need anything, call me. I would like to be your big brother. I know you don't have any brothers, so if you want one, I'm making myself available to you." He handed me his card, patted me on the shoulder, and left.

I put his card in my pocket and went into the house. My grandparents were sitting on the couch, holding each other and crying. I knew something was seriously wrong.

"What is it?" I asked them. They both looked at me through tear-filled eyes. Granddad slid over and patted the couch between him and Gamma. She slid over and smiled at me. I sat down and held my breath. From the looks on their faces, I knew it was terrible.

Granddad took a deep breath and said, "Jer, we have some very sad news. Apparently, your parents have been spending time together for the last few months. They've been involved with some very dangerous people and last night they were found dead in Pikes Point."

I was shocked, but not really. I knew they did illegal things. That's why I lived with Granddad and Gamma. I wasn't expecting to hear they were both dead, though.

"How did they die?" I asked.

"The officer said it looked like a drug overdose," Gamma said, patting my hand. "We're so sorry, Jeremy," she said, and then started to cry again.

"Gamma, it's not your fault." I felt so sad for her. She always blamed herself for my dad's stupid mistakes. I was old enough to know that no one makes you do anything you don't want to. My parents were old enough to know better. I hugged Gamma and looked at Granddad.

"What happens now?" I asked.

"We need to call Jack and Phyllis to see what they want to do about funeral arrangements. They will want to see you, Son."

"I know, but I'm not going to stay with them." Jack and Phyllis were my mom's parents. They never hid their feelings that I was the mistake that resulted from my parents' high school romance. They were nice to me, but I never felt that they loved me. They seemed to always look at me with pity in their eyes. They never missed an opportunity to tell me not to be like my parents. I may only be in the eighth grade, but I know that I don't want to end up like my folks.

The next few weeks went by slowly. We had my parents' funeral together. Then I started school. I was determined to make this my best year yet. This is my last year of junior high school and I needed to make decisions about the future. Every eighth grader at our school had to take a career exploration class. One of our first assignments was to take a test that gave us suggestions about our future. From the test results, we started exploring the top three careers on the list. My results recommended that I explore law enforcement, the military, or social work. I didn't think I wanted to leave Granddad and Gamma to go into the military, so I started with law enforcement. I remembered Officer DeLoach. One day when I got home, I decide to call him. I didn't think he would answer, but much to my surprise, he did. He sounded glad to hear from me and asked if I wanted to go eat pizza. At first, I wasn't sure, but I'm glad I did. He really meant that he wanted to be my big brother. He helped me with my career exploration project and from that day on, we spent time together every week. He coached a little kids' soccer team and asked me to be his assistant. His wife was an acting coach at the local children's theater. She always had some type of building project for us.

I'm in high school now and I'm still friends with Officer DeLoach and his family. I am now a big brother to one of the kids from soccer. His dad was a police officer who was killed in the line of duty. I wanted to be there for him. I'm so glad I didn't throw away Officer DeLoach's card. I could easily have fallen into depression, like some other kids I know at school, but I refuse to fail. Junior high wasn't easy, but I found support through the hardest part of it and now I can see my future very clearly.

CHAPTER THREE
Devan's Rain

I sat in the support group feeling very frustrated and out of place. I'm not like them. I am not abusive. I only pushed my sister because she was getting in my stuff again and my mom freaked out, like she always does. I wish I could live somewhere else.

"Devan, you're being very quiet. Do you have anything to share?" the counselor asked.

"No," I mumbled, and folded my arms across my chest.

"You know that in order to successfully complete this program and meet the terms of your probation, you have to participate, don't you?"

I lowered my eyelids and looked around the circle at the other kids. We all were sent here by a judge because we had hurt someone in our family. Some of them have been here more than once. This was my first time, though.

"I don't know why I'm here. All I did was push my little sister out of my room."

"Your sister has a broken arm," the counselor reminded me.

"It's not my fault she wouldn't let go of the door frame."

"You really don't see the consequences of your temper, do you, Devan?"

"Nope. She's still alive and her arm just has a fracture."

The counselor frowned and studied me for a minute. "Devan, I think you may not be ready for this group yet. I'm going to let the judge know you aren't ready for us."

I was surprised. Was speaking my mind all that I needed to do to get out of this? Cool. I went home satisfied that I was done with that group and would just wait until my probation was over. Little did I know that the judge had something else in mind.

The next week, on Tuesday, I was called into the counselor's office. When I got there, I was introduced to my probation officer. I gulped and sat down.

"Miss Green, I am here because the judge got a message from Mrs. Styles that you weren't fitting in at group. You see, the judge offers support groups for kids who realize their mistakes and are willing to learn how to get along with others. He puts kids who feel group is a waste of time on probation. You are now on probation and will have to serve forty hours of community service."

"What? What do you mean, 'community service'?"

"You have been assigned to Quality Care Assisted Living. It is a home for elderly people who need a place to go while their family works or have other activities that would be too much for them."

"An old folks home?" I asked.

"No, it is sort of like an adult day care for senior citizens."

I frowned at first, and then smiled when I remembered how much fun my granny could be. "Fine. When do I start?"

"You start this afternoon after school. You will spend two hours each week on Tuesdays there."

"What will I do?"

"Whatever the staff gives you to do."

The following four weeks were a blast. I spent two hours every Tuesday playing beauty shop with old ladies. I painted their fingernails and did their makeup and hair. Some of them were really happy to see me and were very nice. Others were cranky and complained about being forced to let a little girl mess up their hair. One lady, Mrs. Griffin, was my favorite. She would come in complaining every Tuesday, but when she left, she was smiling. She told the funniest stories about when she was a teenager. I looked forward to the times we sat together.

One day, she was very excited because she was going to visit her children. They were taking her to a family reunion. I made sure her nails were the color she wanted. The following Tuesday, she didn't come to the beauty shop. I asked her friends where she was. They told me she was in the hospital. I was sad that she was sick and asked my mom to take me to visit her. When I got to the hospital, she had bruises on her face and she had a broken arm. I asked her nurse if she had been in a car wreck. The nurse smiled and shook her head, "No, but I can't tell you. Patient privacy."

I turned and watched Mrs. Griffin sleep. I was glad she was alive, but was worried about her injuries. I visited her for the next three days and each time I was there, she was asleep.

When I visited her on Saturday, she was awake. "Devan, it's so good of you to visit me," Mrs. Griffin said and smiled as I walked into her room.

"Hi, Mrs. Griffin. It's good to see you awake. I was so scared." I held her hand and sat on the edge of her bed.

"What happened to you?" I asked. Her smile faded and I could see tears in her eyes. "You don't have to tell me," I said quickly.

She patted my hand and said, "No, Dear. I'm just sad. My grandson got upset because he wanted to go hang out with his friends, but my son and his wife required him to attend the family reunion with us. I heard them arguing and thought I could help. When I walked into the room, Kyle was storming out and shoved me out of the way. I hit the wall and fell. When I fell, I hit my head and broke my arm."

"That's terrible. I'm so sorry. You didn't deserve that. Are you okay? What happened to your grandson?"

"I'm fine, Sweetie. I'm not sure what happened. I haven't heard from my son today. I understand they sent me the flowers over there by the window."

"Do you mean they haven't been to see you?"

"I don't know. I haven't seen them today. They are busy with their jobs. I understand."

"But you're his mother. He should be here for you," I began, and then thought about how I met Mrs. Griffin. I realized that I was no different than her son and grandson. I was only thinking about myself. I didn't have control of my temper and I could have seriously hurt my little sister.

The following Tuesday, I went back to the support group after I left "Beauty Shop" day at the nursing home. I decided to adopt Mrs. Griffin as my grandma and visited her nearly every day. I'm so glad I did. We have some really fun times together. My mom takes us shopping sometimes, we take flower arranging classes together, and sometimes we go see movies at the classic movie theater. I'm less angry now and make sure I do nice things for my little sister. Yep, my life is so much better now.

CHAPTER FOUR
Logan's Rain

"Mom, I sold a story!" Logan shouted as she skipped into the kitchen.

"You sold a story? What are you talking about?" I asked as I wiped my hands on the dishcloth hanging near the sink.

"I've been writing stories. Mr. Clark told the class about this website we could go to and publish stories. Well, I submitted a couple of stories, and one of them was chosen to be published in a book," Logan explained.

"Honey, that is so wonderful! I am so proud of you. What is your story about?"

"I wrote about Casey."

I looked at Logan with a little concern, "Really? You were okay writing about that? I know you were having a hard time talking about it."

"Yes. My counselor suggested that I write about my feelings and I did. Then when Mr. Clark told us about the website, I decided to check it out. They were having a writing contest and asked for stories about a time when you were in a dark place, but made it through. So, I wrote about Casey. Do you want to read it?" she asked.

I grinned and said, "Of course, I want to read it. My baby is going to be a published author."

"Aw, Mom. Don't make a big deal about it," Logan said and then rolled her eyes as she left to go get a copy of her story.

When she returned, I told her I would read the story after dinner. "You should go call your dad. I'm sure he will want to know." I was so proud of Logan and could hardly wait until dinner was over to start reading her story. She had come a long way in such a short time. Her best friend had died of complications from the flu less than a year ago. Logan was devastated when she found out Casey wasn't coming home. She spent many days crying and refused to leave her room. Needless to say, her second year in junior high was not such a wonderful experience.

That night I waited until everyone was in bed before I sat down to read Logan's story.

Resurrection

The clouds blew in so suddenly that I didn't have time to prepare for the downpour. When I finally made it inside the house, I was soaked and chilled to the bone. It was creepy because it wasn't cold outside. It was actually warm for March. It was the Friday before spring break and I was so excited to have a week off from school. My parents had rented a condo on the Gulf Coast and said I could bring Casey with me. We were going to have so much fun. We had packed everything we would need: journals, nail polish, makeup, magazines, and beach supplies. As I changed my clothes, my phone dinged. I had a text. I knew it was from Casey. She always texted me as soon as she got home from school. We then spent the evening talking or texting about what happened at school. After I finished changing, I grabbed my phone and plopped down on my futon.

Casey: Hey, Logan. I can't go to

Logan: Why not???

Casey: I'm sick. I missed school t doctor says I have the flu. Ugh!!!!

Logan: Oh. I'm sorry you feel bad. I'm going to miss you!!

Casey: Me too.

Logan: It's going to be boring without you.

Casey: Try to have fun. I'm going to sleep now. L8R

Logan: L8R

The ride to the beach was long. I plugged in my ear buds and slept most of the way. Without Casey, it was going to be a long vacation. Going to the beach without a friend is no fun. Casey always went on vacation with us.

Our first day at the beach resort was rainy. We only left the condo to go grocery shopping. I spent the entire day watching movies and texting Casey. The second day was sunny and warm. We packed a picnic lunch and camped out at our favorite spot. After I finished unpacking my tote, I looked around to see if there was anything of interest at the beach. I spotted a snow cone stand nearby and asked my parents if I could go get one. Since it was close enough for them to see me, they said yes. At the stand, there was a group of kids who appeared to be my age. They were very friendly and we sat on the playground equipment to talk. It turned out that two of the girls were staying at the same condo as us. We exchanged cell numbers and made plans to meet at the arcade later that afternoon. I surprised myself because I am usually too shy to talk to people I didn't know. Casey was more outgoing than me. She made friends everywhere she went. "Casey would be proud of me," I thought as I made my way back to my parents.

The next three days were pretty much the same. My new friends and I hung out at the beach during the day and the arcade at night. We went to the movies one night. Every night, Casey and I texted or talked. She was still sick, but laughed at my funny Jet Ski stories with my new friends.

The fourth night, Casey didn't answer her phone and she didn't answer my texts. "Maybe she's sleep," I thought.

The fifth night, my parents came into my room and sat on the bed. My mom reached for my hand and said, "Oh, Honey, we have some sad news for you."

"What is it, Mom?" I asked.

"Sweetheart, you know Casey had the flu."

"Yes, Dad, I know. Is she alright? I've been trying to reach her, but she's not answering."

"She wasn't getting better, so they took her to the hospital."

"Oh, can we go home, then? I really want to be there for her."

My parents looked at each other and I could see tears in my mom's eyes. "What is it, Mom? Why are you crying?"

"Baby girl, Casey died this morning."

"What?! No! She can't be dead! Not Casey! She's my age! She's too young to die!" I cried and hugged my mom. My parents both held me as I cried. I couldn't believe my best friend was gone forever. We left the next day, and the day after that was Casey's funeral. Her parents were so sad. She was their youngest at home. Casey's older brother and sister were in college and lived in another state. It was a very sad funeral. My parents let me stay home from school for two days after the funeral and I had a hard time going back. Everybody looked at me funny and almost no one talked to me. They knew Casey and I were very close. The school counselor called me to the office to let me know I could come see her any time I felt like talking to someone. It was very hard to be at school.

After school, I would go home and curl up on my bed and cry myself to sleep. My parents grew worried after a while and put me in counseling. I liked my counselor, Ms. Brown. She was understanding and she never told me that I needed to get on with life because death was a part of life. I heard some kids say that one day when I started crying after hearing Casey's favorite song in choir.

I made it through the school year and was looking forward to summer break. Instead of taking a family vacation, my parents sent me to a camp for kids suffering from depression. Ms. Brown thought it would be a good idea for me to spend time with other kids my age who were dealing with depression due to the loss of a loved one. The camp was for a week at a lake resort. Ms. Brown was the camp director and there were two other counselors. Our days were filled with team-building activities, crafts, boating, fishing, and hiking.

On Wednesday, we visited a local church camp. The kids at the church camp invited us to work with them on their community service projects. We helped them pack food for Meals on Wheels and packed backpacks full of school supplies for a homeless shelter. We had lots of fun and didn't have time to think about what made us feel sad.

That night, back at our own camp, we gathered around a campfire and talked about what we experienced. Many of the kids thought it was fun and it felt good doing something for someone else. Ms. Brown told us that was the purpose of the experience. She said that on days when we feel the saddest, we should find ways to help someone else. She then gave us a homework assignment: Before our Thursday meeting, we were to write about our darkest day, including what we remembered about it and what we did about it.

As I sat in my cabin, I thought about Casey's funeral. I know I was very sad, but I couldn't remember what I did. All I could remember was the Scripture the minister read at the beginning of the service. He said, "Jesus is the resurrection and the life. The one who believes in Him will live, even if they die." I know Casey believed in Jesus, but how could she live and die at the same time?

At Thursday's session, I shared my thoughts. Ms. Brown asked the other kids if they had any thoughts to share about my question. One girl, Sadie, said that it meant Casey was now living in Heaven. Joshua said that maybe it meant she continued to live in my heart. There were other ideas, but I really liked what Sadie and Joshua said. Ms. Brown thanked us for sharing and gave us another challenge. "Before tomorrow's meeting, write about what you would do if you had another day to live with your loved one."

At first, I thought that challenge would make me sad, but as I started remembering my times with Casey, I didn't become sad. I actually started smiling as I began to write about the time we went on a fishing trip with our dads for a father/daughter weekend. Casey and I really didn't want to go fishing, but our dads wanted to show us how much fun it could be. That trip was a disaster because the tent collapsed when it started to rain and hail. We ended up at a resort hotel ordering room service, going to the spa, and lounging by the pool. Our dads told us not to tell our moms. Casey and I couldn't wait to get home to tell our moms about our "fishing trip."

At Thursday's session, I shared my story and everybody laughed. That night, Ms. Brown gave us each a journal with our name on it. She told us to start writing our memories of our loved ones in it. Whenever we're sad, we should write about a time spent with that person that makes us smile or laugh.

I am so glad my parents sent me to camp. I know that my experience there was the beginning of my healing. I feel totally resurrected."

I wiped away my tears and sighed. Logan had been resurrected after her camp experience. Our little girl was happy again. She made new friends at camp and they get together regularly to talk about their lives and to do various charitable activities in the community.

CHAPTER FIVE
Jonah's Rain

I know I wasn't making the right decision, but I just couldn't do what my father asked me to do. He wanted me to go deliver some books to a poor family from our church. It was embarrassing. I go to school with one of their daughters. I didn't talk to her, but I just couldn't go to her house with those books. What kid would want books about Bible heroes? What would Jessica think of me? So, instead of taking the books to their house, I decided to take them to the church, which was in the opposite direction. I wrote a note on each book and stacked them up near the entrance, where I knew the pastor would see them. When I got home, my dad asked if I'd delivered the books. I nodded and went to my room. I felt guilty about lying to him, but I just couldn't go to Jessica's house.

Two weeks passed without my dad saying a word about the books. I thought I was in the clear, until one night when my dad came home from work and came to my room.

"Son, I need to talk to you about something," he said.

I took off my ear buds and paused my music. "Yes, Dad?" I responded.

"You told me that you delivered the books to the Jennings family a couple of weeks ago, but Mrs. Jennings called my office this morning and asked if I still had a book that her son in college needed for class. Did you deliver the books?"

I lowered and shook my head. "No, Sir."

"Why not? All you had to do was drop off the book bag. David needed one of those books to write his final essay for a class he is taking. They couldn't afford to buy the book. I offered them the book because he needs it to pass a class. What did you do with the books?"

"I took them to the church down the street."

"The church? Why the church?"

"I attached a note for the pastor to give them to the Jennings family. I figured he would contact them."

"I see. You still haven't told me why."

"I was too embarrassed. I didn't want Jessica to think I'm weird."

"Ooh. A girl. Well, Son, not only did you lie to me, but you also delayed the delivery of that book. If we can't find that book, I am going to buy a new one for David and take it out of your allowance."

"Yes, Sir," I said. I knew my dad was mad at me because he closed the door without another word.

As I sat back in my chair, the door opened again and my dad stuck his head in the door and said, "This isn't over." Then he closed the door. I knew I was in big trouble. I felt so stupid. I really didn't have a reason for not taking the books. Jessica didn't even know I existed.

The next day when Dad got home, he called me into the living room. When I got there, Jessica was sitting on the couch. I nearly died. "*Why is she here?*" I thought. I looked at my dad with wide eyes, asking him the silent question.

"Hello, Jonah. Come and join us." Dad motioned for me to come further into the room.

Jessica looked up at me and smiled, "Hi, Jonah."

"Hi," I mumbled.

"I know you are both wondering why I have you here. Well, I think it would be a great idea if you started a reading club." Jessica and I both frowned at my dad.

"A reading club?" I asked.

"Yes. Since both of you seem to be embarrassed about me loaning books to David, Mrs. Jennings and I thought you should start a book club." I looked at Jessica to see if she knew what Dad was talking about.

"Son, you are not the only one who didn't take care of the books. Apparently, Pastor Don called Mrs. Jennings to let her know the books were at the church. Mrs. Jennings sent Jessica to the church to pick them up, but, instead of going to the church, she went to the park with her friends. The books never made it to the Jennings house." Jessica bowed her head. I could tell she was embarrassed.

Dad looked at both of us. We were both looking very sheepish and embarrassed. "You both did something that was very selfish. Mrs. Jennings and I think you need to learn how to think of others before yourselves. Thus, you are going to start a reading club. Pastor Don has a group of young people he has been working with who need something to do. You both are going to read this book, create a plan for starting the reading club, and make the invitations to give out."

"But, Dad, who wants to be in a reading club?"

"Apparently, Pastor Don's group of teens and you are going to make sure it happens for them."

"What is the book?" Jessica asked.

Dad handed us each a copy of "The Success Principle for Teens." Jessica and I both glared at the book and then at my dad.

"*This must be a joke,*" I thought. "How can we start a reading club with this book?" I asked.

"Pastor Don is going to help you get started. You have thirty minutes to get to the church. He is waiting for you. And to make sure you both show up this time, I'm driving you." Dad smiled at us. I could tell he was enjoying delivering this torment on us.

Pastor Don, Jessica, and I spent almost every afternoon together for two weeks, reading the book and creating a plan for starting the reading club. I guess this is what teachers do when they prepare lessons.

The club started in the third week. There were ten kids our age there. Two were from our school and we didn't know the other kids. Our first night was interesting, because we didn't talk about the book at all. Pastor Don told us to introduce ourselves and then left us to talk about whatever we wanted.

It was really fun until one kid nam
that he wanted to kill himself. We al
turned to me and lifted her should
we do now?"

"Dallas, why do you feel that way.
that things at home were horrible and he coul
another way out of it. I asked him if he had told anyone
how he felt.

"No, because my mom doesn't believe me. I don't think anyone else will, either."

"Hey, I believe you. I think you should talk to Pastor Don about it. He's cool."

"I thought about it, but I don't know if I can trust him, either."

"Do you want me to go with you? I will." We all sat quietly while Dallas cried and appeared to think about whether or not to talk to Pastor Don.

"Well, this is the quietest bunch of teenagers I've ever seen in one place at the same time." Pastor Don laughed as he came in pushing a cart with drinks and cookies. He suddenly stopped when he saw the serious looks on our faces.

"What happened?" he asked.

I shrugged and said, "We just ran out of things to talk about tonight." The other kids agreed and got up to get something from the cart.

Dallas, Jessica, and I stayed in the circle, sitting quietly. Pastor Don made his way across the room and sat down next to Dallas, who still had tears on his face.

"Hey, Buddy, what's going on?" Pastor Don asked.

looked at me and I nodded for him to open up.

sighed and asked, "Can I ... Can Jonah and I talk to n the other room?"

"Sure, guys. Jessica, can you take over the refreshment cart?"

"Yes," Jessica replied, and then smiled and patted Dallas on the back. "My pleasure."

We went to Pastor Don's office, where Dallas told us that his mom's boyfriend was touching him in inappropriate places and was trying to get him to do other things. I tried not to look horrified, but my stomach started burning. Dallas was miserable and I understood why. Pastor Don assured Dallas that he would help him and encouraged me to go have refreshments. I didn't want to leave at first because I promised Dallas I would be with him, but Dallas told me he would be okay.

"Thanks, Jonah. I think I'm alright now." I gave him a bro hug and went to join the other kids.

That night I thanked my dad for making me get involved with the reading group. I learned so much about myself in those three short weeks. I learned how to be more confident. I learned that my choices and actions can affect others, and that I am blessed. My mom died when I was little, but my dad takes good care of me. He protects me and encourages me to do my best. I know that if I ever need anything, I can always trust my dad to take care of it.

CHAPTER SIX
Kenzie's Rain

November 15

Dear Diary Friend,

I went to the counselor's office again today because I couldn't stop crying. I tried not to, but I just couldn't shake the sadness, and the tears started when Ms. Banks read a poem in my writing class. I feel stupid crying after listening to a poem, but I did. A boy in my class wrote the best poem I have ever heard by a kid. This is his poem:

"Autumn"
I love everything about autumn.
I love the way the leaves change colors, from basic green to a soothing light red or warm orange.
I love the smell of my mom's cooking as I enter the warm house after a bit of outdoor hoops.
To me no other season can amount to much.
I love fall.
Not even winter, with its long break from school or perfect holiday-themed movies.
Autumn has always been a special time of year for me.
It was when I was born.
It's where all of my best memories are."

Can you believe it? A 7th grade boy writing poetry like that? It wasn't a sad poem; it just reminded me that I have no real talent.

I tried out for the cheer squad last spring and didn't make it, even though I'm on an award-winning competition cheer team. I tried out for volleyball and basketball and didn't make either of them. My parents hired a private coach to help me prepare. We worked all summer through tryouts and I still didn't make either team.

I think the poem just sealed it. I have no talent. I just need to become wallpaper.

Signed,
Invisible Me!

November 20
Dear Diary Friend,

It happened again today. The water works. I didn't go to the counselor's office, but when my mom picked me up from school, I had a meltdown. I didn't get a part in the Christmas play. I practiced so hard with Tana. She got the lead part! Ugh! I knew I shouldn't have tried out, but Mom and Tana talked me into it. I'm not listening to either of them anymore.

Signed,
Invisible Me!

March 30

Dear Diary Friend,

Okay, I know I said I was going to be invisible, bit I did something today that I never thought I would do. I tried out for the spring talent show. Yep, I got up and sang in front a panel of judges and made it! I'm going to sing a song I wrote called, "I May Not Seem like Much to You, But I'm Happy About Me."

Yeah, I know. Happy is a new feeling for me. I haven't had a water works day in two months. After the talent show meltdown, Mom took me to the doctor. She said I wasn't sick; I was just going through a stage in my life. Well, I wanted off that stage! My Aunt Jessa told me that I needed to focus on what I liked doing and put my energy into that. It took a while, but I realized I love to play my guitar and sing. So, when we had a long weekend in January, I began to sing and play for my parents. They encouraged me to keep practicing. I even played at their anniversary party in February. I wasn't afraid to sing in front of our family and their friends. It was fun.

When the principal announced the school was having a talent show in April, Tana talked me into trying out. At first, I said, "No way." I'd made a fool of myself enough times at school. But Tana had a sleepover during spring break and I sang for our other friends. They said I was good and I should try out, so I did.

When I sing, I don't think about what I'm not good at.

Signed,
Stepping Out

April 30

Dear Diary Friend,

I got 2nd place at the talent show! I am so excited!
I know it wasn't 1st place, but I was 2nd out of twenty kids. They were all good.
Aunt Jessa was right. Focusing on what I love to do changed the way I feel about myself.

Signed,
Not Invisible Anymore!

CHAPTER SEVEN
Sadie's Rain

I knew something was terribly wrong. I'd been having the same bad dream off and on for two weeks. They weren't just your typical bad dreams of being chased by monsters or spiders crawling up your arms. In these dreams I was caught up in one natural disaster after another. First I was sinking in a giant hole as the Earth shook in a 7.0 earthquake. Then a super vortex tornado lifted me out of my home. The last dream was an enormous tsunami rising high over the house and washing my family away. As I turned the corner leading down the street to my home I could see three police cars parked in front of my house. *"Great,"* I thought.

I slowly approached the house and saw my little brothers and sister sitting on the curb with a female police officer. Katie was crying. Davie and Jonnie each had an arm around her shoulders. They were always protective of six year old Katie. Davie was nine and Jonnie was ten. I'm the oldest of my parents' four children. I was fifteen at the time and was pretty much in charge of looking out for my siblings. "Hey, guys, what's going on?" I asked.

The police officer stood up and introduced herself, "Hi, I'm Officer English. You must be Sadie." She extended her hand for a handshake.

"Yes, ma'am. I'm Sadie. What's happening?" I asked offering a limp handshake.

"Well, Sadie, there was an incident here today. Your dad was shot and taken to the hospital." As she talked to me she kept an eye on my brothers and sister. Then she started leading me a few steps away from them. She lowered her voice and said, "According to your neighbors, it sounded like your dad was beating your mom. He was yelling while she was screaming and then they heard a gunshot. Do your parents fight often?" She asked.

I hesitated to tell her what really goes on at our house. It was so embarrassing. My parents argued a lot. My dad was always angry or frustrated about something. He complained about almost everything--the food was bland, the house was too hot or cold, the kids were too loud, our rooms weren't clean enough, and sometimes he would ask Mom if we were really his children because we didn't look much like him. He wasn't always like that. I can remember having some really fun times as a family when I was little.

Right after Jonnie was born, Dad got hurt in a car wreck. Mom said he had a traumatic brain injury and it changed his personality. The worse I ever saw him act was when he found out Mom was expecting Katie. He yelled for days about our family not needing any more kids since he couldn't work the same job after the wreck. He slapped mom that night in front of us. I was really scared. I took the boys outside to the backyard and we hid in the treehouse. We didn't come down until the next morning. Dad apologized to us, but I never trusted him after that. From time to time over the next three years, I knew he was mean to Mom when he thought we weren't listening or looking. Every now and then I would see bruises on her arms or scratches on her neck. I did my best to keep the other kids from noticing. When I thought there was going to be an argument, I would take the boys bike riding and push Katie in the stroller to the park a few blocks from our house. I would keep them out for a couple of hours just to make sure the fighting was over before I took them home. If Mom had shot dad, the fight must have been really bad. I looked at the officer and fought the tears that began to well in my eyes. I just nodded. *"Maybe my parents can get some help now."* I thought.

"Sadie, I need you to talk to me. It's very important for you to tell me about your parents' fighting." Officer English said.

I took a deep breath and told her everything I knew. "Can you help them?" I asked.

"I hope so, Sadie. I am hoping we can help all of you. Your dad didn't appear to be seriously injured, but he was admitted into the hospital." Officer English tried to encourage me, but I was scared I was going to lose both of my parents.

"What's going to happen to my mom?" I asked. I wondered if they were going to take her to jail. I still couldn't believe that she shot Dad.

"She is in the house now packing some things for you all. She is taking you and your siblings to a shelter for abused women. You should be safe there. Your father will be released from the hospital in a day or two and she needs to take you all someplace safe." Officer English explained.

"A shelter? Where is the shelter?" I was hoping that I wouldn't have to change schools. I knew a girl who came to our school because her family had moved to a homeless shelter. She had to move away from her friends. I really didn't want to be the new girl at school.

"We found an opening at a shelter in Bridgewater. It's not that far from here."

"Will I get to go to school?" Going to Bridgewater meant that I would have to change schools. I was very disappointed, but I knew it was best for my brothers and sister to be somewhere safe.

"I don't know exactly how that shelter works. Some shelters provide homeschooling for their clients' safety."

"Do I need to go help my mom?" I looked at the house and saw mom carrying suitcases to the car and an officer was loading a box into the trunk.

"Officer Davis is helping her. Why don't you take your brothers and sister over and get them settled in the car?"

We loaded up into the car and waited from Mom. When she finally got in the car, I looked at her. She had a lot of bruises on her face. Her lips were swollen and her eyes were red from crying. She had a patch of hair missing just above her right ear. Looking at her let me know that this fight was the worst ever. I reached out and touched her hand. "Mom, are you okay?"

"I will be, Sadie. I'm sorry. I hate to take you kids away from your home, but I can't go on like this. I need to feel safe and I need to know that you all are safe. I know you have been taking care of them," she tilted her head gesturing toward the backseat, "but that isn't your responsibility. It's mine. I'm going to be the mother you all need from now on."

The shelter was a really nice place. From the street the place looked like an old plantation style house. It made me think of the movie *Gone with the Wind*. It was white with black shutters, tall columns, and a huge porch with a swing and rocking chairs. The house sat on a corner lot and had a white wood fence around it. The yard was pretty with flowers and if you looked at the windows, you could almost picture Southern ladies sitting in front of one of the large windows sipping tea and gossiping about their neighbors (I love to read historical fiction). When we turned the corner, we pulled into the garage of a two story brick building that looked like it had been added to the house.

We were met at the door by a short perky lady with wavy blond hair. "Hi, you must be the Carsons. I'm Nancy. Come in." She held the door open for us. She was very nice and helped us get our things put in our rooms. We ate dinner with the other families in a large dining room. There were four moms and ten kids. I was the oldest. The kid closest to my age was a twelve year old named Sasha. We didn't stay in the open area long after dinner. We were tired and went to bed early. I didn't know what would happen to us next, but for the first time in a long time, I felt safe.

Over the next few weeks Mom's bruises healed and she found a job. The shelter did provide online homeschooling to us kids. Teachers from the local public school volunteered to stop by to help us with our online lessons. One teacher, Mrs. Fugle was an art teacher. She taught us how to do all kinds of crafts. I really liked to paint. She told me I was a natural and she would bring me paint supplies when she came. One day she asked me if I would like to enter a painting in a contest they were having at the local community arts center. I agreed and began to plan my entry. The contest theme was "Peace". Contestants were to create something that represented peace. It took me a few days, but I decided to paint a picture of the front of the shelter. The director of the shelter made sure the place look so pretty. For days I would sit across the street under a tree and look at the shelter. I sketched until I captured the place to my satisfaction. After I painted the picture, I named it, *Safety in a Storm.* When I gave it to Mrs. Fugle, she made a big deal about how pretty it was, but I knew it wasn't that good. What I did know is that I loved to paint and I felt at peace every time I picked up a pencil or paint brush. I didn't win the contest, but I did get Honorable Mention which came with a ribbon.

The time came when we were able to leave the shelter. My mom found a good job in another state and we moved. My dad recovered from the gunshot wound, but he didn't come live with us. He went to therapy and found a job. He apologized to us kids and told us he wanted us to feel safe so he would stay away. We missed him, but our lives were so much happier after we got settled into our new place. I even found an art teacher who owned a studio. I learned more paint techniques and graphic design. She thought I was very good and hired me to work after school to help with her other art classes. I found my peaceful place in art and helping others discover their artistic talent.

CHAPTER EIGHT
Chaz's Rain

Football was my life! I played it, I watched it, and I dreamed about it. On Saturday and Sunday afternoons, if you wanted to find me, there was only one place to look: in front of the tube with a football in my hands. I didn't just watch my favorite teams, either. I watched everybody play.

As a matter of fact, I was so obsessed with football that my room looked like a locker room sitting on a green football field. Yes, my mom was very creative. She painted my room Dallas Cowboys blue and gray. She had green carpet installed. And not just any green, either. Turf green! She found some old lockers and had them installed on one wall along with a bench seat in my walk-in closet. It's the coolest room.

If she went to all that trouble to create my dream room, then why was she taking away my tube time on a Saturday afternoon? I didn't get it. She wanted me to spend time with my little cousin, Titus. He was not that little. He was in third grade. I was playing football on Saturdays when I was in third grade. I wondered why he wasn't. We are a football family. My dad played college ball, my uncle plays for an NFL team, and my cousin Felicity is an NFL cheerleader.

I figured the kid was a geek and his folks, Uncle Jake and Aunt Kara, wanted me to give him the heads up.

When Titus walked into my room, I understood why they wanted me to spend time with him. He was pushing a special walker.

I looked at my mom with my eyebrows raised. She smiled and said, "Chaz, this is your cousin, Titus. He's spending the week with us while Uncle Jake and Aunt Kara go out of town. He has work in California and they are going to make a couple's getaway out of it. Titus, this is Chaz. He is going to hang out with you while you are here." She gave me that "behave yourself" look.

I turned to Titus and said, "Hey, Chaz. Come on in." He stood at the door, looking around my room with an awestruck look on his face.

"Wow, this looks just like Uncle Dave's locker room!"

"You've been to Uncle Dave's locker room? Dude, how did you score that?"

"He probably felt sorry for me and sent us tickets."

"Oh. I'm going to the next home game to watch their game in person. Maybe he will take me to the locker room, too." I smiled. "Do you like football?"

"No. I LOVE football! But, as you can see, I can't play," Titus said with this pitiful look on his face. I thought, *"I'd be miserable, too, if I couldn't play football."*

Titus and I hung out for the week his parents were away. We even got a chance to throw the football around. Titus was really cool. He may not have been able to play physical football, but he was a killer on Madden NFL '17.

A couple of weeks after Titus came to visit, he came to one of my school games. We were playing on a Thursday night. I was glad to see him in the stands. My team was having a great night. We were winning 27 to 0 in the third quarter. I played running back and was running down the field to catch a long pass. I didn't see anyone around me and caught the ball. The next thing I knew, I was on the ground and couldn't get up. I couldn't lift my right leg without sharp pains in my hip. I tried not to scream, but the pain was so bad. I had to be taken to the hospital by ambulance. It turned out that my hip was broken.

I stayed in the hospital for about a week, having surgery and starting physical therapy. I was out for the rest of the season. "*I can live with that,*" I thought. It was just for one season. The time off the field would give me time to get well and I would play again next year.

Three months later, I found out that I should never play football again. I was crushed. Not only could I not play football, but the doctor also said that all sports were off limits for me. I was messed up after that. I didn't go anywhere and I asked my mom if I could redecorate my room. Of course, she told me no. I only went into my room to sleep after that.

One day Titus came over and asked if I wanted to go outside to throw the football. "Haven't you heard? I can't play football anymore?!" I snapped at him. I felt bad because it looked like I'd hurt his feelings, but I really didn't want to go outside. Titus didn't say anything else to me for the rest of that day.

A couple of weeks later, Titus and his family came over again. This time he didn't ask me to go outside. We played video games, but not Madden NFL. At the end of the day, just before they were leaving, Titus asked me, "How long are you going to feel sorry for yourself because you can't play football?"

I didn't answer him, but watched him slide his walker across the floor and walk down the hall to the join his parents.

All during the next week, I thought about what Titus said. I didn't think I was feeling sorry for myself. I had a right to be upset. I wouldn't ever again get to do what I've wanted to do all my life.

Wednesday night we went to church and we had a guest speaker. He was a former marine who had been severely injured and had to leave the military. He told us that he had always wanted to be in the marines. He gladly served in the Gulf War and serving in Afghanistan pumped him up. He was proud to be fighting for freedom. Everything was going great until one day, his combat team was caught in an explosion. Lt. Jones lost his hands, but three of his team members died. He talked to us about being thankful for what we have and how His faith in God helped him face life after having to leave the military. He told us that sometimes the plans we make are not God's plan for our lives. Lt. Jones told us that sometimes God allows things to happen to us so that when we recover from the setbacks and disappointments, we can help someone else who may face similar circumstances. He said that it didn't do any good to stop living because we face setbacks. The best way to get over the disappointment is to find a way to serve others. When we are focused on others, we don't have time to focus on our own sorrows. He also said that just because one dream doesn't come true, it doesn't mean all of them won't.

I only had one dream. Football was my future. I needed to find something else to do. The next time Titus came to visit, we did toss the football around and he introduced me to coding for digital games. I'm not only feeling better, but I also now have a new skill to explore for my future.

CHAPTER NINE
After the Rain

I wrote this book for young people because every year I meet some wonderful kids who are having a tough time dealing with life. Some of them suffer from medical conditions they have no control over. Others have broken school and society's laws and need someone to give them a fresh start. There are other kids who appear to have everything they could ever want, but don't know how to get along with others. There really is no specific formula for making life better. The key to making life better is to never give up on hope. Hope is like rain. Hope can refresh the dry places in your life. Hope can restore your lost faith. Hope can energize you to create something extraordinary. Hope can change your outlook on life. Hope can ignite a passion in you that can flood your life with more possibilities than you could imagine. Reach for hope.

ACKNOWLEDGEMENTS

Cover art provided by Raymond Troumbly

Interior illustrations provided by the following Hallsville Junior High School Art students:

Chapter 1: Sydnee Stubblefield

Chapter 3: Kaylyn Arnold

Chapter 4: Alex Hutson

Chapter 8: Alexis Wickey

Poem: *Autumn* by Taylon Mosley

ABOUT THE AUTHOR

Cindy Mosley is an inspirational author and teacher. Her writings focus on encouraging young teens to discover their talents and ways to be an encouragement to others. Her mission is to spread the Gospel through messages of hope. She reaches out to her adult reading audience through poetry, short stories, and devotional writings on her blog cimowrites.com.

Cindy is the daughter of Curtis and Betty Dudley. She and her husband, Frank, have five children and seven grandchildren. Cindy and Frank live in Longview, Texas.

CPSIA information can be obtained
at www.ICGtesting.com
Printed in the USA
LVOW11s1338220318
570802LV00001B/39/P

9 780692 802236